My Village in France

Not far from Avignon, the famous medieval town in the south of France, lies Théziers, a village that is the home of only a few hundred people. Young Denis Martinesse has always lived there, surrounded by vineyards that give good wine, rich cherry orchards, fields of hay and potatoes edged with cypresses, and hills covered with olive trees and fig trees. Two years ago he left school to help his father in the fields—he is expert with the tractor—which he much prefers to a job in the village brick-and-tile factory.

In this book Denis tells about his big family and about the history and daily life of the village he knows so well. He crisscrosses the neighborhood on his motorcycle, plays *boule* with his father and brothers, stops at the eighth-century church of St. Amand, and cheers the bicycle race (a trial for the Tour de France) that passes through the village. On Sunday Denis and his friend Jacques make a motorcycle excursion to the Pont du Gard, the bridge and aqueduct built by the Romans, and then on to Avignon, with its own celebrated *pont*, the one in the well-known folksong.

When he is done, the reader will feel that Denis is a friend and that Denis's home is almost as familiar as his own.

Church of St. Amand

Bakery

The Martinesse house

Olive trees

Potato field

Old vineyard
("Grand-père")

A.M. JAUSS

Also by Sonia and Tim Gidal

My Village in Austria
My Village in Denmark
My Village in England
My Village in Germany
My Village in Greece
My Village in India
My Village in Ireland
My Village in Israel
My Village in Italy
My Village in Morocco
My Village in Norway
My Village in Spain
My Village in Switzerland
My Village in Yugoslavia
Follow the Reindeer
Sons of the Desert

My Village in France

SONIA AND TIM GIDAL

PANTHEON BOOKS

The authors gratefully acknowledge
the cooperation given to them by the
Department of Foreign Affairs in Paris.

Library of Congress catalog card number: 65-12644

My Village in France

I

My name is Denis — Denis Martinesse . . . ah, but I should say *"Bonjour!"* before I introduce myself. "Good day!"

I live in a village called Théziers in the South of France, in Provence. I have one sister and four older brothers. Roland is a carpenter, Yves is working on the railroad. Henri is already married — he and Jean-Pierre both work in the brick and tile factory down in the valley, along with our uncle Joseph. They make good money, but Jean-Pierre dreams of going to Paris one day and becoming a painter.

Jean-Pierre paints a lot, but not very well if you ask me. I know, because Jean-Pierre collects picture postcards with paintings by famous artists who lived in Provence too. Paul Cézanne, for instance, and Vincent van Gogh and Paul Gauguin and Auguste Renoir and Raoul Dufy—they were great painters! Sometimes I can recognize the places they painted.

Van Gogh and Cézanne almost never sold a picture, Jean-Pierre told me, and still they never gave up. But Jean-Pierre would give up painting quickly, I think, if he couldn't make a living from it. I know that much.

My sister, Danièle, dreams of going to Paris too. She wants to become an airplane stewardess and see the world. But nothing doing, of course, for the time being. Maman is very strict about such funny ideas. A girl belongs in the kitchen, she says, and all she needs for a happy life is cooking and sewing, making cherry *confiture*—cherry preserves — cultivating flowers, and keeping the house tidy. "*C'est comme ça!*" she says. "That's how it is!"

Maman is a bit old-fashioned, and Danièle can be stubborn. This time we brothers are all on her side. "But we are only five brothers against *one* Maman," we always say, and we keep quiet.

Then there are our dog, Dolly, and our cat, Miquette, and our mule, Ninette. And our ferret, Perfume — *oh là là*, does he smell! That's why we gave him this name.

We are quite a big family. Most of the other families in Théziers have only two or three children. As for me, I am very glad to be in such a crowd at home. For instance, if it were not for this, I wouldn't have my new Mobylette, my motorcycle. Everybody chipped in to help me buy it after I had saved up half of what it cost myself. I didn't even have a birthday at the time.

I am the youngest in the family, so they spoil me a little, I suppose. *C'est tout* — that's all. And I, I don't mind a bit. It's so much faster to go to work on my Mobylette, and much more fun than walking every day.

I have been out of school for two years already, working with Papa

3

in the vineyards and in the fields. But I work for other farmers too, helping with the cherry harvest, driving a tractor, giving a hand in the orchards or with house repairs. I like this much better than working in the brick factory. It gives me more time for reading too, especially biographies.

When I was still in school, my teacher punished me when she caught me reading under the desk, but now that I am out of school, she lends me all the books I want. *Voilà, c'est comme ça!* — There, that's how it is!

Today, Mademoiselle Faisat is going to give me a book about the scientist Louis Pasteur. I'll pick it up at the school when I bring her back the biography of the Marquis de Lafayette which I finished yesterday. What a great man he was!

My aunt Thérèse is visiting with us now. She comes from Auvergne, a mountainous region in the heart of France, where she lives in the same village in which Lafayette was born — he lived there in the big castle of his forefathers. I read up on the Marquis so I can tease Aunt Thérèse a bit with my knowledge of him. She is always talking about her village and about Lafayette; it sounds almost as if she were *his* aunt too, or as if she owned him.

Our village is not known for anything special. No great man was born here, and no battles were ever fought over the place. It wasn't worth it, it seems. But our vineyards give us good wines, we have good potatoes from our fields, we have very good cherries and fine tasty tomatoes, and we have the brick factory. Nothing special, really, except our big white cherries. The best *confiture* in all France is made from them!

We have red-cheeked juicy peaches and apricots in our orchards, and in our gardens we grow big artichokes and *aubergines*, or eggplants, and cucumbers, onions, and garlic. The hills around us are covered with olive trees and fig trees, and our meadows can be mowed

for green fodder and hay three times and even four times a year.

Still, our village isn't a rich one. It's really very fortunate that we have clay soil in the neighborhood. This is the reason they could build a brick and tile factory down in the valley. About sixty of the two hundred and fifty grownups in our village work there, and they bring home their nice weekly pay every Saturday, come rain come shine.

It's really very good to have a paycheck every week, no matter whether it is sunny outside or rainy, and even when hailstorms destroy the harvest. Still, I would rather be on my own as a farmer, and I'd rather work in the open than in the factory.

Our house has six rooms. I share a room on the third floor with Jean-Pierre. Roland and Yves sleep in the other room there. Danièle is lucky — she has a room all to herself on the second floor, next to my parents' bedroom. On the ground floor is the *salle*, our big living-and-dining room with the kitchen corner. The front door leads straight into it. The small room at the back of it has shelves for the jars of preserves, and a sofa. Aunt Thérèse sleeps there right now.

Our windows look out toward the east and the west, but the north side of the house has no windows at all, so the mistral wind can't blow in and plague us. It is a pest, that mistral! Sometimes it blows so hard it tears the tiles from the roofs. And even on the hottest summer days, it can make you shiver to your bones with cold.

The mistral destroys the young plants and blows precious topsoil away if you don't take precautions against it. It blows at least three days every week, and whatever else happens in the world, we talk less about it than about the mistral. Everybody in the village does, everybody in the whole of Provence, I guess. But sometimes even the worst mistral isn't all bad. After a rainstorm, for instance, it dries the ground quickly, because it is always a dry wind, and so it keeps the vegetables and the roots of the vines from rotting. I just hope it won't blow too hard tomorrow — I want to go on an outing with my friend Jacques.

Maman's roses would not survive a single day of a strong mistral, if we hadn't put up a wall of reeds on the north side of the path leading to the house, to protect them. The roses are Maman's special love.

Just now she is binding them up again — but all of a sudden she lets out a shriek and puts a finger in her mouth.

"I pricked myself good this time," she laughs. "*Voilà* — no roses without thorns, I guess."

I wince, because that's Maman's favorite saying, and we hear it at least once a day.

"Shall I write it on our wall calendar, Maman?" I tease her:

>"There is no rose without a thorn,
>
>There is no foot without a corn . . ."

"*Your* foot, perhaps, eh?" Maman retorts. "Be careful you don't get corns on your cheek if you get too cheeky for once! Ah, my roses, my roses! I wish I could grow whole fields full of them, the way they do down on the Riviera, where the mistral doesn't blow so badly. Millions and millions of flowers are grown there for the perfume factories at Grasse and Paris — jasmine and violets and mimosa and lavender, as far as the eye can see. Imagine, Denis, it takes thousands and thousands of flowers to make the tiniest bottle of perfume. Ah, what a scent they give, those flowers!"

7

"Our onions and garlic have a scent too!" calls Papa from the other side of the road, where he is working in the vegetable garden. "What's wrong with *them*?"

"Scent! It's just like you and the boys to talk like that! Those things don't have a scent, they have a smell, you fools! But what's the good of talking to men about perfume? I'm glad I have at least Danièle to talk to about . . . and I don't say I don't like us to grow garlic and onions."

"And our artichokes are not so bad either, eh?" Papa says. "And when you cook us a fine dish of *aubergines* with cheese and pepper and garlic, it tastes better than a bunch of roses, *n'est-ce pas,* Denis — isn't that so?"

"*Certainement!*" I answer. "Certainly!" But Maman just shrugs her shoulders in mock desperation. "That reminds me," she says. "Denis, get me some pepper from the grocer before lunch."

"We have a lot of work in the vineyards today," Papa adds. "Take the tractor down to the 'Grand-père.' I will follow you soon with Ninette and the plow."

"*Oui*, Papa," I answer, "yes, Papa," and mount my Mobylette. The "Grand-père" is our oldest vineyard. Grandfather planted it more than sixty years ago, and Papa named it after him.

II

Dolly basks in the sun, and Miquette sits in the shade. They don't even bother to move when I come up. Those lazybones know I will go around them. Dolly just turns her head to see whether it is worth

her while to bark at least, but she doesn't. The sun makes her too lazy even for that.

I honk my horn to startle Dolly out of her morning dreams, and ride on. Our village really does look deserted. It is cherry-picking time, it's potato-harvest time, it's haying time — everybody is out working, except the children in school.

I pass the old archway under the clock tower. The ruins of the ramparts, the tower, and our church of St. Amand are all that remain of an old fortress that once stood here. It was built in the eighth century against the Saracens who came over from North Africa and looted the prosperous villages of Provence.

When our teacher told us about this, she always added: ". . . but nothing much seems to have happened in our village since then, except for the cobbler who was killed under the old arch. They never found out who killed him, or why."

I often think of the cobbler when I pass here, and if it happens to be night, I get gooseflesh, and say a short Ave Maria for his poor soul.

My friend Jacques sits on his motorcycle and grins at me.

"*Bonjour*, Jacques! *Comment ça va?*" I greet him. "How goes it?"

"*Ça va,*" he answers. "All right. Surprised to see me here, eh?" Of course I am surprised. Jacques is an electrician's apprentice in Montfrin, a village ten kilometers away.

"I just phoned my boss for help," he tells me. "Last night the lights went out in the church, and they asked us to find the cause. Seems there was a short circuit because of some faulty line up on the ram-

9

parts. I can't repair it alone, because I don't have enough wiring with me."

"I'm not sure *you* could repair it even *with* enough wiring," I tease him. "And how does your chic motorcycle feel today? Is it ready for the outing tomorrow?"

Jacques's is really a much heavier and more powerful motorcycle than my light Mobylette.

"Never mind mine," he answers. "You just nurse your babylette, so it won't cry when I go a bit fast. By the way, I saw a poster over at Aramon village. They are giving a historical play about that old

King René in Aix-en-Provence tomorrow. With a hundred horses and a real tournament, it seems. Shall we go there?"

"*Entendu*," I answer. "Agreed. But first I'll have to take a few jars of cherry *confiture* to the restaurant at the Pont du Gard. I promised Maman — they should have been delivered days ago."

10

"Good enough," Jacques says. "Let's meet at eleven o'clock tomorrow. How about the cypress tree below the rocket station?"

"Fine," I agree, "and I will ask the baker to make us a loaf of bicycle bread to take with us."

We call it bicycle bread, because it has a very big hole that makes it convenient to hang over the handlebars for a *pique-nique*, a picnic. It is made from wheat flour and is as white and crisp as all our bread. Bread is our staple food; we eat it with every meal.

Danièle is just coming from the baker with our daily ration of five *flûtes*, our long thin loaves of bread.

"Are you two twaddling again?" she says. "Hey, you circus urchins!" she suddenly shouts, and Jacques and I are startled.

"Not you!" Danièle laughs. "Although you can be clowns too at times. Just look at those crazy acrobats over there! Hey, what are you doing? You'll break your necks soon. Why aren't you in school, anyway?"

"We have a bad cough," Fernand and Jules answer in chorus, with a grin, "and Maman went cherry picking."

"And you are going back home at once, or I'll tell your teacher," Danièle threatens them, and I start my motor and follow them home. Then I race to our shed.

Our shed is an old stone building opposite the school. There we keep our machinery: the plow and the tractor and the vine sprayer, the cart and the tools. Our ferret Perfume has his cage there too, and Ninette's stable is partitioned off by a stone wall. The hayloft is above the shed.

I put my cowboy hat on. Aunt Véronique gave it to me. She lives down south in the Camargue, a marshy region at the mouth of the Rhône River, where her husband is a mounted guardian on one of the big bull-and-horse ranches that make the region famous.

I climb up on the tractor, and when the motor starts clanking, I drive out through the village. At the public trough, where the village women wash their laundry, Madame Mathieu signals me to stop.

"Denis," she calls, "you boys are experts in noises, *n'est-ce pas?* Tell me then, was that a jet plane just now, or a hail rocket?"

"All I heard was the noise from my own motor," I answer, while I look up. "But there's a large dark cloud with a white border around it. That's a hail cloud all right, so it probably *was* a hail rocket you heard."

I really must ask Papa how it works. All I know is, they shoot rockets at the cloud to disperse it, and then the hail doesn't come down on our vineyards but somewhere else. The other winegrowers don't like that, I suppose. I am sure there is something wrong with my explanation, but Papa will know.

"*Merci, mon ami,*" says Madame Mathieu. "Thanks, my friend. That was my opinion too, when I heard the noise. But Madame Lisette, ah, she always thinks it's the jet planes making a nuisance of themselves when she hears a big noise."

I drive down the winding road to the plain. The young vineyards don't need much care now, except for being sprayed with chemicals to protect them from the insect pests. The mistral won't harm them either; the rows of cypress trees on their north side is high enough to break its force, so all it can do is dry the ground. But when I come to the "Grand-père," *oh là là*, that is another matter altogether. The vineyard is so overgrown I hardly can recognize the furrows between the vines.

I couple the plowshares to the tractor and start loosening and turning the sandy soil with them.

Meanwhile Papa has arrived too. He took the steep, winding path down from the village. Our mule can manage the narrow, steep road, but the tractor never could.

Papa starts plowing another vineyard with the mule.

Sometimes Ninette gets stubborn and won't move. Then Papa only has to shout "Catherine!" at her — and the mule goes on! Nobody

knows why Papa gave Ninette this second name or what makes her so obedient when she hears it, but it always helps.

Papa never tells us this secret, much as we pester him about it. He just smiles and says: "Everybody wants a nice secret all to himself. *Eh bien* — well, then, this is mine."

Back and forth we work our way through the vineyards, Papa with Ninette and I with the tractor. It is getting very hot, and the work is tiring. But after three hours or so, I am through with the "Grand-père" at last.

I wave my hat to Papa and drive back. On the way, Monsieur Michel stops me.

"Denis, look over there! Ernest Dessis has really bought that new spraying machine he kept talking about all the time. He can spray in an hour what it takes me a full day with my old contraption here. Where did he get all the money from, I wonder? I can't afford it. I don't know — some people have all the luck, it seems."

"Ah, there goes old grumpy again!" Madame Girard calls over from her wagon, where she is sorting out cherries. "Why are you always complaining and envying, always this and always that! Perhaps it's

your own fault you are not more successful."

"How do you mean, my own fault?"

"Ernest couldn't afford a new spraying machine either, and you know it. But he got together with my son André and a few other friends, and they bought the machine together and they take turns using it. They even make money by spraying for other people too."

"My wine doesn't bring me enough money for renting other people's machinery, and I, shall I look on idly meanwhile? *Alors* — now, if we were in the Rhône Valley, where the wine brings twice as much money as ours, that would be another story!"

"But we are not. That's why *we*, for instance, planted cherry trees too, and they grow better here than anywhere else in France. Look how big and healthy they have come again this year! There, take a few handfuls. Cheer up and stop worrying for a change, Michel. Worrying won't help you and it spoils your appetite. I know you put your money in your old stockings like a miser, instead of investing it in new machinery."

"Maybe, Madame Girard, but —"

"But, but, but . . . come on, eat!" And now even old grumpy can't help smiling, while he munches the cherries. I get a handful too. They taste very good.

"I really wouldn't dare to put so much money into a new machine," Michel begins again. "How do I know it will pay?"

"If we kept out new machinery and new inventions, we soon would lose the sale of our wine altogether," I put in. "We might as well

start plowing with a wooden plow instead of a tractor. Since Papa bought this one, we can work three times as much land as before, and from the extra money, Papa has already bought two more vineyards. It won't be long until our village can afford a co-operative wine storage like so many other villages have. And with that we can think of bottling the wine in our own plant under government supervision. Then we can export it to Germany and to America too. You will see us prosper yet, Monsieur Michel, if you and more like you will stop complaining and hoarding their money in old stockings."

"Listen to the chick telling the hen how to lay eggs! If we don't save —"

"I know, I know!" interrupts Madame Girard excitedly. "It's an old French habit to hoard savings instead of investing them in new enterprises. But it is a bad habit, I tell you, and those young people who are changing it are right."

17

As for me, I am surprised myself at the long speech I just made, and while the two are going on with their discussion, I drive on to catch my uncle Joseph at the brick factory.

I pass the clay pit, where a huge bulldozer is pushing the brick clay forward. It looks like a tugboat making its way through a sea of white sand.

Gustave works the excavator. The big bucket comes down, the teeth bite into the loam and lift it up to the waiting truck. The truck carries the brick clay to the brick and tile factory.

We try to call to each other, but our two vehicles make such a tremendous noise that we have to give up and just make signs. It looks funny, like a movie when the sound breaks off. I wave to Gustave and go on to the factory.

From the two huge chimneys smoke rises into the sky, but the building is almost obscured by huge stacks of roof tiles and bricks.

Not long ago, only twenty workers were employed here. But now at least sixty men work day and night in the factory, because so much building is going on everywhere.

My brother Jean-Pierre has the night shift this week. He works from midnight till eight o'clock in the morning. Uncle Joseph is on the day shift, and in the evenings he is the village cobbler.

I walk up to the second floor. There I find him stacking white roof tiles on a shelf.

"*Bonjour!*" I greet him. "*Comment ça va?*"

"*Merci*, Denis," he answers. "*Ça va*. What brings you here? Do you want me to show you the factory? Are you getting interested at last, eh? I always told you you could make good money here."

"Oh no! I'd rather stick to my work in the open," I answer. "But you know, Uncle, I am going with Jacques Labourayne on an outing tomorrow . . ."

". . . and you want your sneakers for it, is that it? *Bien*, you will have them this evening."

"*Merci*, that's nice of you, Uncle Joseph. And Uncle, since I am here anyway, do you think I could have one of those roof tiles there? One of ours was swept off the roof by the mistral a few days ago, and broke."

"Could you have one of these! Denis, you really don't know anything about this place. It's a shame! Come, I will explain it to you. When you step on a roof tile with heavy shoes, what happens?"

"Nothing — unless I jump very hard on it, and then of course it breaks."

"*Alors*, now step very lightly on this roof tile here . . ." and he puts it on the ground. I do as he says — and the tile breaks as if it were of thin glass. I am really startled, but Uncle Joseph laughs.

"You didn't expect this, eh? *Alors*,

the tiles here have just come from the machine. On one side, the clay dough is fed into it, and pressed through the die. At the other end, the molded roof tiles come out. They are sent up here on the conveyor belt, and I store them in this warm hall till they are more or less dry. But they are still crumbly, as you have seen. Only when they have been fired in the kiln at a temperature of about two thousand degrees Fahrenheit do they become hard as stone and get their reddish color. It's like leaving bread in the oven for a day. You would have to use a hammer to break it apart."

"Where are the kilns?" I ask.

"Down below. Come with me."

We climb down the steps and walk along a wall with many openings. Some are closed up with bricks. We step through a low opening into a kind of cellar room.

"*Mon Dieu!*" I exclaim. "My God! It *is* hot here!" and I feel the sweat breaking out all over my face and neck and body. "It must be at least a hundred degrees!"

"Say a hundred and forty, and you are closer to it," Uncle Joseph says with a grin. "Nice and cool, isn't it! And this room has been ventilated for twenty-four hours already. After all, you are inside a

20

kiln now — when the bricks are being fired, the temperature goes over two thousand degrees in here."

He takes bricks from a pushcart and stacks them up high.

"This is how we fill the kiln with bricks and roof tiles," he explains. "And then, after the kiln has been hermetically closed, the bricks and tiles are fired. I'll show you. Come out with me again."

He leads me to the next kiln. A worker is closing the entrance to it with bricks, and smearing mortar over it to make it airtight.

"This kiln is now ready for firing," Uncle Joseph says, "so I'd better go upstairs and get ready. When we open it up, another big load of bricks and tiles will be ready for transport. Interesting?"

"*Eh oui, certainement!* But I think I still prefer not to work in a factory, Uncle."

"*Chacun à son goût,*" he laughs. "Everybody to his own taste. *Au revoir* — goodbye, then, till tonight."

"*Au revoir,*" I answer, and go off. I step on the gas and race to the village as fast as my tractor will go. *Chacun à son goût!* That's a good one. I must remember it.

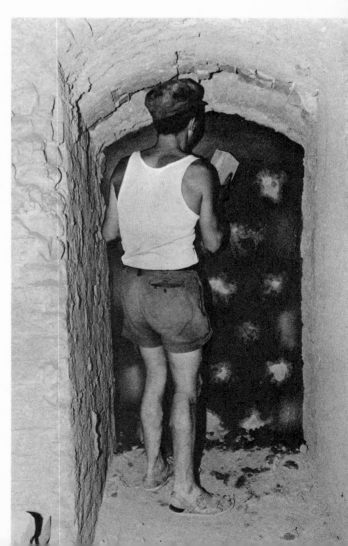

III

"*Écoute*, Denis — listen!" shouts our postman, Florent, to stop me. "Mail for your aunt again! Please take those two postcards along for her, and save me the walk to your house."

Florent Savinas is not only our postman; he also takes charge of the postal savings bank and is the public telephone operator of the village, when he isn't out delivering mail.

Our mayor has a telephone of his own, and the policeman of course, and the priest. Three or four of the village notables have one too. All the other villagers go to the post office if they want to telephone.

"Look at this funny postcard for your aunt, Denis! It comes from Ambert village. The man here seems to be hanging up some sort of laundry. Much too small for bedsheets. They look like big diapers, *n'est-ce pas?*"

"*Mais non!*" I answer. "But no! They make precious art paper in Ambert village in Auvergne. You wouldn't believe it, they make the paper there by hand, exactly the same way they did it six hundred years ago. It's the oldest paper mill in France, perhaps even in the whole world. My uncle Michel explained it to me once when I visited him. He works there, and took me along. Once he brought Jean-Pierre a few of those sheets for his water colors. They are made for artists like Picasso, who print their lithographs on them — it is the best art paper in the whole world. The man in the picture is just hanging the large sheets of paper up for drying. Do you know what they make this expensive paper from? From old rags!"

"Shining white paper from dirty old rags!" Florent exclaims. "I don't believe it."

"It is true, though. The rags are bleached white and torn into little

shreds. Then they are mixed with water and crushed to pulp with wooden hammers. There are about ten of those heavy hammers in a row, and they are driven by a turning wheel, and the wheel is driven by the water running past the mill."

"Never mind the wheel, Denis. I know what a mill is, but what does it do with that pulp?"

"The pulp looks like porridge. It's poured out over big square sieves, where it settles into a sort of thick felt. Then the water is squeezed out in a press and the sheets are hung up till all the remaining dampness has evaporated. It's more complicated than I can explain, of course."

"You explained it well enough for me, Denis. I must read up on it in my encyclopedia; it sounds very interesting. Perhaps I can go to Ambert on my next vacation and look at that old paper mill myself. The other postcard comes from Chavaniac-Lafayette. That's where your aunt Thérèse and your uncle Michel have their home, *n'est-ce pas?*"

"*Oui,* and it is the fourth or fifth time she's got that same picture of that same castle where Lafayette lived. It seems they don't have another postcard in their village."

"*Écoute,* not every village can boast a Marquis de Lafayette. Tell me, didn't you say last week that the picture postcard with the white horses came from your aunt?"

"Ah, *oui*— but I have aunts living all over France and even in Spain. Madelon, Pauline, Georgine, Bourdette, Marie, Mélanie, Véronique, and Thérèse — that's all, if I remember rightly. Aunt Véronique is the one who sent me the cowboy hat."

"It looks comfortable enough. Look at mine, it keeps falling over my ears. But what can I do — it was given to me by the main post office. They probably thought I have a big melon for a head."

"So why do you wear it?"

"*Mon Dieu!* Caps have to be worn on official business. *Alors,* maybe it will get lost one of these days!" and he laughs.

"Have you got more picture postcards today, Florent?"

"Not many. I can offer you the Eiffel Tower once again, this time at night. Quite an achievement to flood it with light all the way to the top, I must say. It's almost a thousand feet high, after all. Do you see the pavilion up there? It holds eight hundred people, and on top of the iron structure is one of the strongest broadcasting stations in the world. What else do I have today? Let's see. Ah, this is a beautiful one of prehistoric paintings in the caves around Les Eyzies. Did you read the book about how a boy and his dog discovered the cave of Lascaux? The most beautiful of all cave paintings were found there."

"*Ah oui,* I know about it. I wish I knew how those people twenty thousand years ago made the colors to do these paintings."

"And I wish I knew how they liked living with these paintings on their walls all the time, those strange animals and bulls. . . . That reminds me, there's a bullfight in the Roman theater at Arles tomorrow. I am going over to see it. Are you?"

"*Non,* I am going on an outing with Jacques Labourayne. *A bientôt,* Florent — see you soon!"

"*A bientôt,* Denis!"

I race to the shed and park the tractor. Then I buy the pepper for Maman and go home for *déjeuner,* our lunch. It smells of cabbage in the *salle.* That means Aunt Thérèse has cooked one of her Auvergne dishes again. And with an Auvergne dish always go her stories of what else is better in Auvergne, which means almost everything. They have sixty dead volcanos there, she tells us, and two hundred thermal spas for rheumatism and the like, and five hundred old castles. But I wouldn't swap our sunshine and blue sky for all her volcanos and old castles and what not. We don't have thermal spas, but we don't have rheumatism either. My aunt brags a bit, but otherwise she is really very nice.

Papa pours us some light wine. We drink it with every meal, and I like to mix mine with water.

We do have cabbage again, with *aubergines,* bacon, and sausage, seasoned with garlic and pepper, and it tastes delicious. With it, we

eat salad and white bread. "White bread, salad, and wine keep you healthy," Maman always says. "...and garlic!" we shout then, in chorus.

A tractor passes by. The motor stops and somebody calls: "Madame Martinesse! Madame Martinesse!" Through the open window, I see our mayor step down from his tractor and begin unloading crates full of freshly picked cherries.

"Ah, *Monsieur le maire!*" Maman calls back. "I am glad you came. The last cherries are all in the jars already."

"I smelled your cabbage *pot-au-feu*," he teases. "I wish my wife would learn how to make this kind of cabbage stew."

"Send her over," Aunt Thérèse answers. "I will be glad to teach her the dish."

Monsieur Adrien is not only our *maire*; he also owns the big cherry orchards down the road, and on the side, he is an insurance agent. During the picking season, he always sells a few crates of cherries to Maman, apart from the thousands of pounds he sells to the famous *confiture* makers at Marseilles and Paris. Maman sells her preserves

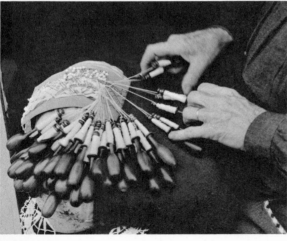

to a few restaurants. "From the tree to the jar on the same day makes the finest preserves," she says.

We have fresh cherries for dessert, and then I go up to my room and leaf through the book on Lafayette again, before I take it back to my old teacher. I want to surprise Aunt Thérèse with *my* knowledge for a change. She sits in the open door, working away at a lace coverlet with her bobbins.

"I forgot to give you these two postcards, Aunt," I say.

"Ah, *c'est bon*," she replies. "That's good. I love mail. Where are they from? Read the postmarks to me, please."

"One is from Lafayette and the other from Ambert."

"Put them in my pocket, Denis. I can't read them now, with all the bobbins hanging."

"I get dizzy when I watch you throwing the bobbins around. How can you tell what order to use them in?"

"Ah, that is easy, once you have learned it. Look at the pattern on the paper underneath the lace here. I have drawn the design and pricked it to show where the pins should go.

"Along the lines of the design, I twist and cross the thread-wrapped bobbins. Watch now — down goes a pin to hold the design in place. That's all. If you did it for a few centuries, it would be easy for you too."

"A few centuries?"

"*Oui*. Ever since the sixteenth century, the girls in Auvergne have learned lacemaking, when they were ten or twelve years old. In that century, pillow covers, tablecloths, and coverlets of lace were very fashionable. No man or woman would have dared go to a wedding or any official gathering without a high collar and cuffs of the finest lace. Ah, those were the days!"

"Awful days, if you ask me," I say. But instead of getting angry, Aunt Thérèse breaks into uproarious laughter.

"What's so funny about it?" I ask — and I am getting annoyed. I didn't laugh at *her* old-fashioned ideas, after all. But my aunt almost chokes with laughter and just points the other way. I turn around, and start laughing myself.

"Carro!" I shout. "You glutton! You will get a stomach-ache!" But it is too late. Carro has already eaten up heaps of the cherries, it seems — fruit, pit, and stem. Now he licks his lips after his delicious dessert, and runs away.

As soon as Carro has gone, Colette jumps on Aunt Thérèse's lap. She must have had an argument with Miquette, or she wouldn't have been sulking in the kitchen all this time. Aunt Thérèse brought her along all the way from Chavaniac-Lafayette in a wicker basket, and Miquette is still jealous of her.

"Ah, *bonjour*, Madame Thérèse, *comment ça va?*" calls Monsieur Isoard, who is just strolling by. Off duty, he never wears his uniform, except for his official cap with the GC on it, the initials for *Garde Champêtre*, Country Policeman.

"Ah, little Colette is here too! *Comment ça va, ma chérie?*" Monsieur Isoard says. "How are you, my dear? Don't you want to get your paws into the lace a little bit?"

"What a dreadful idea, Monsieur Isoard!" Aunt Thérèse says sternly. "Colette is a gentle cat and a well-behaved cat — not at all like some tomfools I happen to know . . ." and she throws him a meaningful look.

Oh là là — that was a sharp rebuff for our *garde champêtre*!

"*Mais, madame,*" he replies, "but, *madame*, I was just teasing a bit. Here in the South, we like to have fun. You people from the Auvergne hills, you take every word so seriously. Oh no, I wouldn't encourage your Colette to do anything naughty — or you might call

the *garde champêtre*, eh?" and he laughs heartily, and winks at me. Aunt Thérèse really is a bit fussy at times.

Clément Isoard guards the vineyards and the orchards, the roads and the fields and the village. He makes his rounds four times during each twenty-four hours. He starts out at four or five o'clock in the morning for his first round, sometimes even at two or three. He always changes the hours and the route so that poachers, if there are any around, won't know when to expect him. The *garde champêtre* is also in charge of the hail rockets.

Aunt Thérèse and Monsieur Isoard both look down their noses, as if they don't quite know how to forget their little dispute. That makes me feel uncomfortable, and so I try to get a conversation going. But what shall I start with? Ah — Lafayette! That will do it.

"Monsieur Isoard," I say, "do you know that in the castle at Chavaniac-Lafayette, they still keep two pistols which the President of Washington gave as a present to the Marquis de Lafayette?"

"It wasn't the President of Washington," Aunt Thérèse corrects me. "It was the first President of the United States of America, and George Washington was his *name!*"

"*Mais merveilleux!*" Monsieur Isoard exclaims. "But that is marvelous, how you know about these things, *madame!*" I can well see he is out to pacify her.

"How should I not know," she answers, "when I clean those pistols once a month!"

"You clean the pistols in the castle? How does this come about?"

"Ah, *bon,* I am in charge of all the rooms there. I dust the gilded snuffbox Lafayette received from the City of New York, I clean the pin he got from Benjamin Franklin, who was a very important person too at the time. And in the Connecticut room, there is even a ring from that same President Washington with a lock of his own hair and a lock of his wife's." She looks proudly at us while she tells us all this, almost as if the presents had been given to her.

"What is a Connecticut room?" the *garde champêtre* asks.

"Thirteen big rooms in the castle are named after the thirteen original states of the United States of America," I tell him, "and Connecticut was one of them." Out of the corner of my eye, I watch my aunt while I say this. She makes big eyes.

"The Marquis had helped the Americans in their fight for independence from England, and they made him a general to show how grateful they were."

"And how do *you* happen to know all this, *Monsieur le professeur* — Mr. Professor?" Aunt Thérèse asks suspiciously.

"*Alors,* I must have read something about it years ago," I say non-chalantly, but inside, I beam.

"Come to think of it," Monsieur Isoard remarks, "I too remember a story about the Marquis de Lafayette. He was a very great French-man indeed, I think. *Écoute.* One summer, the crops had failed around the villages where he had his estates, but the Marquis's gran-aries were still full from the last year's harvest. Food was scarce, and the coming months looked hopeless.

" 'Now is the time, sir,' his supervisor suggested, 'to sell your grain to the farmers at double the price!'

" 'Oh no! Now is the time to give it to them free,' Lafayette cor-rected him."

"I didn't know this story," Aunt Thérèse puts in. "What a noble gesture . . . and do you know he became a general when he was only nineteen years old?"

"I won't make that any more, I am sure," the *garde champêtre* says and laughs. "How did he manage it?"

"He was a captain of the dragoons in the French army then. At a dinner party, an English duke, or someone like that, told him about the rebellious colonists. 'Wouldn't you like to fight there?' he asked him. 'I would,' answered Lafayette, 'but on the side of the Americans, because they fight for independence!' "

"That was a very good answer!" I put in. "I hadn't heard about it before."

"You hadn't heard about it before!" Aunt Thérèse mocks me. "And what *have* you heard before?"

"*Bien,*" I continue her story, "Lafayette was very rich. He bought a ship, named it *Victoire,* and packed it full of weapons. The English heard about it and interceded with our King Louis XVI. Lafayette was arrested. But his friends sailed the ship secretly to Spain and he himself escaped in disguise. With eleven good friends and a full crew he sailed to South Carolina in the year 1777 and joined the re-bellious colonists."

"Are you trying to tell me you read about all this years ago and remember it word for word? I'll tell you what I think — you looked it all up today or yesterday just to impress me, you little swindler!"

"Yes, I just read a book about him," I now confess laughingly, and I show it to them. She really seems to think Lafayette belongs to her and nobody else!

"I have to run now," I say. "*Au revoir!*" And with that, I go over to our shed.

Papa stands there looking up at the sky and gesticulating to Attilio, Gaston, and Deloye.

"*Mon Dieu!* Another hail cloud!" he exclaims. "They are shooting off a rocket again. Ah, I hope the rocket hits it right and breaks up the cloud, so the hail doesn't hit our vineyards."

"A hailstorm couldn't come at a worse time," Deloye agrees, while he puts his glasses back on his nose. "The vines are at their most delicate stage now. This morning I saw a small dark cloud with a white border around it. 'That means hail,' I said to my wife, 'if they don't catch it.' But they did fire a rocket up in time."

"*C'est vrai!*" adds Attilio. "That's true!" And he puts on his beret, which fell off when he craned his neck to look up at the hail cloud. "What a wonderful invention this rocket shooting is," he says. "It has saved us from quite a few hailstorms already, *n'est-ce pas*?"

"*Certainement!*" Gaston agrees. "As for me, I do not understand at all how it works, this shooting at clouds. Well, I'll stick to shooting at rabbits, anyway. That reminds me — how is your ferret doing, Antoine?"

"I don't know," Papa answers, and I give him Perfume, whom I have just fed. Papa holds him up. "We give him his bread soaked in milk twice a day, but somehow Perfume is a bit listless."

"Same as mine," Gaston remarks. "I suppose they are longing for a few rabbits' heads."

"*Eh bien,* they will have to wait till we go hunting again," Deloye says. "Did you dull his teeth with a file?"

"Denis did it this time. I want him to get used to the ferret — and the ferret to him."

"I forgot it last year, and my ferret killed a few rabbits inside their burrow . . ."

". . . and fell asleep there, and didn't come back for two full days — instead of chasing them out alive." Papa laughs. "Don't I remember! We helped you watch the holes till your ferret came out at last."

Papa's friends go on their way, and I put Perfume back. Gaston returns and calls into our shed: "Antoine, don't forget to come to Arène's Café on Sunday for our game of *boule.*"

"I won't," Papa answers, and to me he says: "Do you think Perfume recognizes you yet?"

"I am sure," I answer. "He even listens when I whistle. Papa, do you need me any longer now? I want to go over to the school and pick up a new book from Mademoiselle Faisat. And afterwards I want to watch the bicycle race."

"I will go down to see it myself," Papa answers. "By the way, your back tire looked a bit flat to me this morning. Did you check both tires?"

"Oh, my Mobylette works fine, Papa. No need to check it so often."

IV

I leave the shed and walk over to the big schoolhouse. One of the classes is just lining up by twos at the foot of the stairs.

"What are you doing out here so early?" I call down to my cousin Marie. "The bicycle race doesn't start till four o'clock at the earliest, you lazybones."

"Lazybones yourself," Marie calls back. "We are going to the church for our history lesson."

"And I am going to the Bridge of Avignon to play *boule*," I tease back.

The boys and girls shout "Nonsense!" and under Marie's lead, they start singing:

Sur le pont	On the bridge
d'Avignon	Of Avignon
L'on y danse, l'on y danse,	People dance there, people dance there,
Sur le pont	On the bridge
d'Avignon	Of Avignon
L'on y danse tout en rond.	People dance there in a ring.

But then their teacher comes out and hushes them up.

I dash upstairs to the second floor and knock at the door. "*Entrez!*" I hear Mademoiselle Faisat call. "Come in!" And I walk in.

"Ah, Denis," the teacher says, "you brought the Lafayette book back, I see. Here is the one on Louis Pasteur I promised you. Does anybody here know the connection between the milk we drink and Louis Pasteur?" she asks the girls and boys, who are drawing and painting. Some of them keep looking out of the window and I am surprised the teacher doesn't reprimand them.

"Pasteurization!" one of the boys says. "Milk very often carries diseases. Louis Pasteur discovered that all the dangerous bacteria in the milk are killed when you heat it almost to the boiling point and let it cool again quickly. This process is called pasteurization, after Louis Pasteur."

"*Formidable!*" exclaims the teacher. "Excellent! You can be proud of yourself, Charles. Pasteur made many more discoveries. For instance, he invented the inoculation against rabies and that is how thousands of people all over the world are saved when they are bitten by mad dogs. *Alors,* you will read about all this in the book, Denis."

37

While Charles and the teacher talked, I took a look at one of the drawings — it is the house across the street. So this is the reason the boys and girls turn their heads toward the window. Stupid of me not to notice it earlier.

"Merci beaucoup, mademoiselle," I say, "thank you very much," and I leave the classroom. In our schools there is class from eight o'clock in the morning until five-thirty in the afternoon, with a two-hour break for lunch. At least, there is no school on Thursdays and Sundays — that helps. Even so, it was always hard for me to sit still on a bench for most of the day. No, I like to work in the open air.

On my way back, I pass the class, walking quietly by twos.

Suddenly a window opens, and out looks Madame Breton. I know well what's going to happen now . . . and indeed, she starts beating time with her arm and singing the national anthem:

> *Allons, enfants de la patrie!*
> *Le jour de gloire est arrive . . .*
> Forward, children of the fatherland!
> The day of glory has arrived . . .

38

Madame Breton has been doing this silly thing ever since I can remember. Whenever a group of children passes her window, she sings the *Marseillaise* to them, the song of the French Revolution.

"Come on, sing with me, children!" she calls down. "You march better when you sing our national anthem." But the children only start giggling and laughing.

"Madame Breton," the teacher calls back, "*La Marseillaise* is for special occasions, *n'est-ce pas,* and not just a marching song. And we don't want to march like soldiers anyway."

"*Eh bien,* have it your own way, then," says Madame Breton. "But woe to the child of France who doesn't know his *Marseillaise . . .*" and with that, she slams the window shut.

"Madame Breton means well," the teacher tells the children, "though she is a bit strange sometimes."

For months now Madame Breton has been carrying on a fight with *Monsieur le maire,* because a lot of paint has come off the words RÉPUBLIQUE FRANÇAISE on the wall of the *mairie,* the mayor's office It is not dignified, she says, that the FRENCH REPUBLIC should peel off. But *Monsieur le maire* says, "Nobody is afraid of the French Republic losing dignity, so don't fuss about the paint. It's what is in our hearts that counts." I think he is right, but it really *does* look a bit decayed. The whole building needs a new layer of plaster and fresh paint.

The children have now arrived at the church square. Their teacher shows them how the church was built into the thick walls in early medieval times, and tells how these walls once surrounded the whole village and made it into a real fortress. She explains how the people could seek safety there when the Arab warriors came to plunder the countryside. The high clock tower, she says, was originally a lookout tower with a parapet.

A strong light comes through the open door of the church. From above the door, a stone sculpture of Saint Amand, the patron saint of our village, looks down.

I walk in and see Jacques and two other electricians working on the switches and electrical lines. *Monsieur le curé*, the priest of the church, is there too.

I still have time before the race, so I just stroll around in the church. I say "Hello" to Jacques, and watch him and the other electricians testing the lines and changing bulbs.

Five or six children peek in through the open door. Their history lesson seems to be over, and the other children have all gone home.

"Look, Jeanne d'Arc is lighted up much more than ever before," one of the boys says.

"You are right," says *Monsieur le curé*, and then he explains: "We are having stronger floodlights installed while the lines are being repaired. The old ones were very weak."

It's true. In the strong new light I can see we really have a nice statue of our *Sainte de la Patrie*, the patron saint of our country. She wears a knight's armor and a tunic embroidered with the royal white lilies. In her left hand she holds a sword, and the right one grips the lily standard of the Kings of France.

"Step over here, boys and girls," *Monsieur le curé* invites them. "I will tell you something. Have you ever considered *why* Jeanne d'Arc became a saint?"

"She drove the English from our country," a girl answers.

"That should make her a national heroine, but not a saint really."

True enough, I think, while I listen. Or else it should be *Saint* George Washington. After all, he drove the English from *his* country.

"She did it because the Archangel Michael told her to," one of the boys now says.

"Correct! She said she heard voices from heaven, and that God wanted her to free her country. She was a country girl of only seventeen when she convinced the soldiers and officers and even the crown prince himself that God had chosen her for this task."

"And then she made the crown prince King of France, *n'est-ce pas?*" somebody asks.

"More or less. The Dauphin, as the crown prince was called, was a timid man. He was afraid of the English. But Jeanne d'Arc asked him to trust in God and in her. She made him go to the town of Reims, and there he was crowned King of France in the cathedral. I've told you already, he was a timid man — he betrayed Jeanne, but she went on fighting for his cause. When she was taken prisoner by the enemies ten months later, he even refused to pay ransom for her.

"It's a terrible story. Jeanne d'Arc came before a clerical court and was accused of heresy and witchcraft."

"What is heresy?" one girl asks.

"Heresy is a belief different from that of the ruling church. The bishops and priests of the court thought it a crime for Jeanne to insist that she had heard heavenly voices. But Jeanne insisted again it was the truth. She would only listen to God and her heavenly voices, and to nobody else."

"And how was she a witch?"

"She wasn't, of course. There are no witches except in fairy tales. But the judges said that only by witchcraft could she have persuaded the Dauphin and the officers and all those thousands of soldiers to follow her to war, a simple girl who couldn't read or write. Her voices must have come from the devil, they said. In the end, she was sentenced to die, and was burned alive at the stake. But even then she cried out: 'My voices are from God . . . everything I did, I did on God's orders . . . my voices did not deceive me.'"

Our *curé* goes on to tell how the people of France more and more believed that Jeanne d'Arc had been right and that she had been killed unjustly. In the end, about five hundred years later, she was declared a saint by the Catholic Church. "This happened in the year 1920 . . . but now you'd better go, children, or you will miss the bicycle race."

The children thank the *curé*, and leave, and I too say "*Au revoir*" to him and to Jacques and walk home for a snack. I know most of the story of Jeanne d'Arc, but it always grips me whenever I hear it. I am glad that in our time it isn't a crime any more to have thoughts of one's own. I can say that much.

V

After I have eaten, I ride off again. The streets are now full of people who have interrupted their work and are walking or driving down to the highway. I stop at a slope from where I can get a good view of the race. Most of my friends are there already.

We don't have to wait long. Michel sees the cyclists when they are still only tiny spots on the horizon. "Here they come!" he shouts. They race so fast that soon we can recognize their faces.

"Look, there is Pierre!" Jean-Louis cries. "The one with the dark glasses — he is sixth!" Pierre is from our village, and we all hope he will finish among the first three.

"*Non*, he is seventh!" I exclaim.

"*Un! Deux! Trois!* Pierre! Pierre! Pierre! — One! Two! Three! Pierre! Pierre! Pierre! Go! Go! Go!" we cheer him on and clap our hands, and Pierre puts a thumb up at us and grins as he passes. Soon the group is in the distance again.

"Look! Look! Pierre is swerving to the side!" somebody behind me shouts. "What's wrong with him? He is falling! Oh, *mon Dieu*, he is falling!"

We all start shouting with excitement. This is terrible! Pierre really has swerved to the side of the road and fallen down. He gets up again, looks at his bicycle, and rubs his left leg. He limps a few steps, but then he swings himself onto his bicycle again and follows the others.

We look at each other in consternation. What has happened?

"They will tell us tonight, when they come back," says Monsieur Raoul, the butcher. "It didn't look right to me. That boy worked so

hard. 'Two or three more years,' he said to me, 'and you will see me in the Tour de France.' He is ambitious, that boy, and he has very good lungs."

"*Eh bien*, Raoul," remarks Florent, the postman, "that will be the day, when one of our boys makes the Tour de France. Racing through the whole of France! Over forty-five hundred kilometers in seventeen days. That's not a four-hour ride around Avignon! Did you watch the last Tour de France on television? It was marvelous, how they raced across the country."

"Ah, *oui*! I went to a friend in Avignon and saw them on the last stretch, as they came into Paris. There must have been millions of spectators on the highways and streets."

"I watched it too. That Jacques Anquetil was a sight, wasn't he! Five times he's won the yellow *tricot*, the yellow sweater of the Tour de France. Five times the victor, and five times the first prize — more than thirty thousand *francs* each time. *Pas mal*, eh? — not bad!"

I haven't seen the Tour de France on television, but our whole family followed it on the radio, and I read all about it in the newspapers.

It's time for me to drive over to Uncle Joseph's house, to pick up my sneakers.

"*Bonjour*, Denis," he says. "Did somebody really jostle Pierre?"

"How do you know something happened to him?" I asked surprised.

"*Écoute*, there *are* people who are faster than you. Was he jostled?"

"I don't know. Nobody saw exactly how it happened."

"Except for our *garde champêtre*. He was here a few minutes ago to pick up his boots. He thinks he saw something fishy. He has very sharp eyes, don't you know that?" And he laughs.

"Don't I know it! He almost caught René and Jules last week."

"Pity he didn't. They were poaching, weren't they?"

"Ah, *bon*, Uncle, that's a hard word. They just came across that rabbit by chance. It would have been a pity to let it fall prey to some fox, *n'est-ce pas?*"

"It is closed season now," my uncle answers. "They shouldn't have done it. Anyway, here are your sneakers."

"Papa! Papa! I found a snail again!" my little cousin Henri calls from outside.

"If we could eat Henri's snails, I would always have enough for the seven of us without working. He finds this same big plastic snail about twenty times a day!" Uncle Joseph exclaims. "Ah, Henri," he calls back, "bring it to Maman and tell her to cook it, and not to forget the spices. But first, show it to your cousin Denis!"

We often eat snails. Real ones, I mean. We find hundreds of them in the vineyards after a good downpour. I like them best cooked with garlic and served with tomato sauce.

"Take Danièle's shoes along too, Denis," Uncle Joseph tells me. "You know, she walks very straight, not shuffling along as you do."

"I never knew I shuffled!"

"But you do. You always wear down your soles before the heels are used up. But your sister, she uses up heels, soles, and toe-tips evenly, because she walks straight. Old shoes tell you a lot about their owner."

I take both pairs and thank Uncle Joseph and ride off on my Moby-lette. At the church square, the *garde champêtre* is talking with Jean-Pierre and a few others.

"Was Pierre jostled?" I ask them.

"That's what we want to know too," says Raoul the butcher, and Monsieur Isoard adds: "We'd better wait till Pierre returns!"

I rattle on over the cobblestones. I wish they would repair the road

for a change — I feel every bump — and I start railing at our *maire*, at the village council, and at the government for not taking better care of the roads. It's getting so bumpy I have to dismount — sure enough, there is no air in the back tire! Ah, *bon*, I should twist my own nose, it seems, because I didn't check the tires when Papa warned me this morning.

I push my Mobylette the last few hundred meters to the house.

"What a sour face you're making!" Danièle laughs. "Anything wrong? Ah, you have brought my shoes, *merci!* I am just pressing your shirt, that's the last one, and I am glad I am through. I want to start setting the table for *dîner*."

"I had to push that darned Mobylette of mine — a tire went flat," I grumble. I wash and put on the freshly ironed shirt and walk outside to fix the tire. But there is Papa already, taking off the back wheel.

"Bring me a bucket of water," he says. Papa loves repairing things. I pump air into the rubber tube while he dunks it in the water and turns it till bubbles come up. "There's the puncture!" I say.

The hole isn't too big. We sandpaper the area around it, and glue a small patch of rubber over it. After the glue has dried, Papa helps me put the tube back into the tire. I screw the wheel back on, and pump the tube up. It seems to be all right again.

"*Merci beaucoup*, Papa," I say. "I hope it will hold tomorrow."

"Let's hope for the best," Papa answers. "Danièle, where is Maman?"

"She went to the *boucherie* with Aunt Thérèse. Denis, when she comes home and sees you wearing that fresh shirt already, there will be trouble. You'd better change."

"At Madame Mathieu's *boucherie* they are," Papa calls. "That

48

means a late *dîner*. Shopping there means gossiping till every one in the village has been dealt with properly."

"Papa, Denis, please, are you ready?" Jean-Pierre calls. "We want to start playing! You *know* we want to beat the Arnauds tomorrow at the *boule* match. Let's have some practice."

"They always threaten us with winning next time," Papa laughs. "*Voilà*, they haven't succeeded yet. Let's start."

50

Yves hands each of us three heavy steel balls. Every set has a different design embossed on it, so they cannot get mixed up.

Jean-Pierre starts. First he throws a small wooden ball, the "target" ball, between six and ten meters away. Then he tosses the first of his three steel balls after it and tries to place it as close to the target ball as possible.

"Could be worse!" he exclaims.

"Could be better!" Yves adds.

Now it is my turn. I have teamed up with Papa. I hold the ball underhand, swing it, aim, and let it sail through the air . . . oh, bad! It hits the ground even further away than Jean-Pierre's did.

Yves comes next, his ball comes closer. And now Papa . . .

"*Oh là là!*" I exclaim. "You are not in form today either, Papa."

"Patience! Patience, Denis. I haven't even started yet."

The game goes on. In the next round, Papa comes closest to the target. "*Parfait!*" I comment. "Perfect!"

"*Pas mal,*" Papa says, "but there are too many pebbles on the ground for the ball to backspin."

"I am not sure Papa is closest," Jean-Pierre objects. With a length of straw, he measures the distances from Papa's and Yves's balls to the target.

"You are closest, Papa," he says. "Your team gets a point."

We continue, and in the end, Papa and I have scored fifteen points against eleven of Yves and Jean-Pierre. We have won, because we have reached fifteen points first.

"*Alors*, you will have to buy us drinks, losers!" Papa says laughingly. "You know the rules, *n'est-ce pas?*"

"*Oui! Oui!* We all know the rules, Antoine!" Maman calls. She stands in the road with Aunt Thérèse, and both have their hands full with heavy baskets. They have come back from buying provisions at the *boucherie*, the butcher's shop.

"Come on in," she continues. "I'll buy you all a drink — a home-made drink. It won't cost you a *centime*, either."

"Ah — brandy grapes!" we shout. "Ah, your brandy prunes! Ah, your brandy cherries!"

"Ah, my water from the faucet!" Maman answers. "If you want to tease me, you can drink a big glass of water, winners and losers alike." But she is already putting the glass jars on the table. The grapes have been soaked in strong brandy for months, but for the prunes and cherries, Maman uses light brandy only. Danièle and I take the prunes, the others the grapes.

Then we eat our *dîner*, our dinner. Maman and Danièle serve us with a big plate of boiled ham and cold cuts, garnished with tomatoes and lettuce. They put bowls of green and black olives on the table, and Maman brings in the cheese on the beautiful olive-wood plate she got from Aunt Bourdette, who lives in Spain. My favorite is the round peppered goat cheese, which comes wrapped in vine leaves.

"Oh, Denis, I have ordered the bicycle bread for you," Danièle tells me, and I thank her. But otherwise, we only talk about Pierre's bad luck at the bicycle race today.

After dinner, my brother Henri and his wife drop in for a chat, and a few neighbors too.

"Have you heard?" Henri reports. "Pierre says he collided with

Renard from Aramon village, all right, and that threw him off. But whether he was jostled or not, he cannot say for sure. And Renard says the same of Pierre."

"Nonsense!" I say angrily. "Pierre wouldn't jostle anybody."

"And the people of Aramon say that Renard wouldn't jostle anybody," Henri answers. "Anyway, Pierre tried his best and came in seventh, and Renard ninth. The judges let it go at that, because it might have been nobody's fault."

We discuss the case for a long time, and then I start my new book on Louis Pasteur, while the others go on talking. "*Bonne nuit*," I say at last. "Good night."

Miquette sits outside on the window sill and mews. I bring her a bowl of milk, and then I walk upstairs and go to bed.

VI

I wake up at nine o'clock. Everybody in our family wakes up late on Sundays, except Maman and Danièle. They go to church.

As on all Sundays, I prepare my own breakfast, a cup of coffee and a piece of white bread with cherry *confiture*. Afterwards, I pack the provisions Maman has prepared for my outing — some goat cheese, olives, tomatoes, a piece of sausage, and a bag full of cherries. All this and the six jars of *confiture* for the restaurant at the Pont du Gard, I stow away in the leather bag of my Mobylette. Then I ride on to the *boulangerie*, the bakery.

It is open on Sundays, but closed on Mondays. A few churchgoers are there to pick up their freshly baked *flûtes*, but I don't see my bicycle bread on the shelves. So I step down to the basement.

"*Bonjour*, Gilles," I call to him. He stands half naked in front of the oven. It is hot here, but not nearly as hot as in the kiln yesterday.

"*Bonjour*, Denis!" he calls back. "I am almost through for today. Only the crowns and braids are still to be baked. Everything else is ready: big *flûtes*, medium *flûtes*, small *flûtes* — light brown, medium brown, dark brown, anything you want."

"Anything I want? I want my bicycle bread, Gilles."

"Oh, *mon Dieu!* I forgot it, of all things. Really, Denis, I meant to make it first, even before I started anything else. My thoughts were with Pierre's accident instead of your bread. I am sorry, Denis!"

"*Eh bien*," I answer, "it can't be helped now, can it? What do *you* say: was it Renard's fault?"

"I don't know — but I know Pierre came in seventh, and again we didn't make it, and that's bad!"

"We will have to wait for next year — can't be helped, Gilles," I say. "I have to run now. *Au revoir!*"

The clock strikes eleven when I come out of the *boulangerie,* and at eleven o'clock I was supposed to meet Jacques! I step on the gas and race down to the highway and on to the tall cypress tree below the rocket-firing station.

"Late again!" Jacques teases me. "You always make me wait when we meet." I ruefully admit it.

"But what is worse," I add, "Pierre came in seventh. And what is still worse, Gilles forgot to bake our bicycle bread."

"And what is the worst of all," Jacques exclaims, "your back tire looks flat."

"Oh, *non*, it is all right now. I just didn't blow it up enough."

I take out my pump and make up for it.

"Off to the Pont du Gard now," I say. "Let's go!"

We speed along the highway; Jacques lets me go in front. We pass first the orchards of our village. Everywhere people are picking the

last cherries of the season. Then the road goes up, and now we look down over the orchards and vineyards and fields and vegetable plots, and the rows of cypress trees which protect them by breaking the onrush of the mistral wind.

We pass people bringing in the hay, and others who are digging the new potatoes from the ground.

It is Sunday, but people are at work because the weather forecast hasn't been too good. If it should start raining hard or, even worse, if hailstorms should come down, the harvest would be ruined.

At last we arrive at the Pont du Gard, the bridge over the river Gard. We stop at the restaurant there, and I deliver the six jars of *confiture.*

We are eating ice-cream cones at one of the souvenir stands, when a man looks out of his foreign car and asks in broken French: "Tell me, young man, is that the famous aqueduct up there on top of the bridge?"

"It's the Pont du Gard," I answer, and Jacques adds, "The famous Roman bridge. The road on it has just been repaired; you can drive over it again."

"*Merci beaucoup,* my friend,"

the foreigner says, and he and the others in his car get out. They look at the bridge, and he reads something to them from a guidebook.

"Aqueduct, he said?" I ask Jacques. "What is the aqueduct?"

"If you won't give me away — I don't know either. It's a shame, really. Come on, let's buy one of the booklets over there at the souvenir stand." This we do, and then we sit down on the bank of the river and read:

The bridge and aqueduct over the river Gard was built by the Romans in 19 B.C. The bridge is still used for traffic. The purpose of the aqueduct on top of it was to bring pure water from distant springs to the city of Nîmes. The water ran through a covered channel on top of the bridge, which prevented evaporation through exposure to the sun.

The word aqueduct comes from the Latin words *aqua* (water) and *ducere* (to lead). Aqueducts were constructed either below ground or on the surface, or on top of solid walls, or, as in this case, on arches.

The Pont du Gard is the finest Roman aqueduct in existence. 49 meters (about 160 feet) high and 275 meters (about 900 feet) long, it was constructed of heavy stone slabs without the use of mortar. The single slabs, which weigh up to seven tons each, are kept together in this marvelous construction by sheer weight and balance.

"Look!" I shout. "A repair man is up there on top!" and I point to the right side of the aqueduct, where I see a man walking along.

"Don't be silly," Jacques says. "They stopped using the aqueduct hundreds of years ago, I am sure — or we would have known *something* about it. Some tourist has climbed up there. Shall we go up too?"

"*Non*," I answer. "Not today. You know my Mobylette isn't very fast; we would lose too much time."

"*Entendu*," Jacques assents. "Let's go on, then." He steps on the gas and speeds off. I try to catch up with him, which is not easy at all, since his machine is so much more powerful than mine.

In the next village, Jacques stops in front of a *boulangerie*. In the window a few alligators and snakes are displayed, a hare, too, and other pastry.

"Let's get some bread in here," Jacques suggests. "We'll want to eat our *pique-nique* soon."

"We are just closing," the baker's wife tells us. "I am sorry, there is only a loaf of bicycle bread left. You can have it, if you are content with it. The *flûtes* there I need for my family."

I look at Jacques, and he looks at me. Of all things to be offered — bicycle bread!

"*Oui!* Of course we'll take it," I say. I reach into my pocket, but I have run out of small change, and so Jacques pays. "I'll give you back half of it later," I tell him when we leave the *boulangerie*.

"*C'est drôle!*" I exclaim. "That is funny! The only bread she had, and it was bicycle bread!"

"As if it was waiting just for us," Jacques says and hangs it over his handlebars. Then we ride slowly down the village road.

"Look over there, Jacques! The procession of the bottles!" The procession walks up the hill to a chapel. The wine-growers carry the bottles to

have the wine in them blessed there by the priest.

"Let's look for a place to eat now," I say to Jacques. "I hear a rumbling in my stomach."

"Wait a minute, Denis. Do you see that poster over there? Let's look. It's an announcement: 'Historical Reconstruction of the Entrance of King René into Aix-en-Provence.' Do you think they will have real horses and real sword fights, Denis?"

"I don't know. You can't learn sword fighting in heavy harness in a few weeks, though — that much I know. In medieval times, they trained for years."

30.31 mai
Jeux de la Fête-Dieu
Reconstitution Historique de l'entrée du Roi René
Aix-en-Provence

VII

We ride out of the village, and stop at the roadside. A big herd of sheep is grazing on the meadow. This looks like just the right place for our *pique-nique*.

It is really hot now. We sit down in the shade of the cypress trees which shield the meadow and the sheep from the mistral. We take out our food, cut the bread into large pieces, and start eating. From our aluminum bottles, we drink the mint lemonade we have taken along.

"Not a soul here," I comment. "The sheep are guarding themselves, it seems."

"Oh, that white goat over there is watching the herd," Jacques replies dryly.

"Maybe she is watching *you!*" I retort.

"Meh-eh-eh-eh-eh-eh!!" comes a bleat from behind the cypress trees.

We jump up, a bit startled, and look through the dense branches. An old man sits on the grass and laughs. "Did I frighten you?" he asks. "*C'est bon* — that's good! *I* am the goat that guards the sheep, I, Antoine Poignac of the village of Angles. Oh, I interrupted your *pique-nique*, it seems. Come sit with me, it is lonely here. *Bon appétit* — a good appetite to you!"

We move over and offer him bread and cheese and sausage.

"*Merci beaucoup*, boys," he says, "but I have just eaten. What kind

62

of cheese do you have there? Ah, that's goat cheese. Come, try my Roquefort." And with that, he takes a piece from his shoulder bag and offers it to us. It's very tasty.

"This sheep cheese is not from around here," I say, "*n'est-ce pas?*"

"Certainly not. My sheep here are raised for wool. The only Roquefort cheese worth its name comes from the sheep in the region of the Massif Central. They have better pastures there in the neighborhood of Roquefort village. You know, they age the cheese in those caverns at Roquefort for at least a month. My brother is a cheese taster there; he often sends me a parcel of the best.

"Where are you heading?"

"Aix-en-Provence," I say.

"Ah, to the historical *fête*! But you should have gone there yesterday, boys, when the tournament was on. Today is only the procession." He takes out his watch hanging from a long gold chain. "Look, it is two o'clock already. You will be late anyway, if you don't go right now."

"*Au revoir*, then," we say, and mount our motorcycles.

"Nice old man, that shepherd," Jacques shouts to me, while we ride side by side. "He did give you a fright, eh?"

"Who, me?" I shout back. "Ridiculous!" . . . and I step on the gas. The roads are empty now. They always are during these hours when everybody is home having a nap after *déjeuner*.

Suddenly, it gets bumpy . . .

but the road is smooth! Oh, *mon Dieu!* I am losing air again!

"*Halte! Halte!*" I shout to Jacques, who is way ahead of me. "Stop! Stop!" and I honk my horn. A few meters ahead, just at the cross-roads, he stops.

"I am losing air, Jacques," I mumble, and I start pumping like mad. I am furious now.

"*Tonnerre de Dieu!*" he explodes. "God's thunder! At the worst possible moment you have to lose air, just when we are in a hurry. Why don't you travel in a baby carriage!"

"*Écoute*," I say meekly, "I patched the tube only last night. I thought it would hold."

"Thought! Thought! Don't think so much, it's not your strong point anyway," he bellows. "Let's go to Avignon, then. It's only thirteen kilometers away, and I know a repair shop there that might be open.

You go in front, Denis — I don't want to lose you!"

A few times I have to stop on the road and pump the tire up, but at last we arrive at Avignon. Jacques takes the lead now because he knows the town. We ride along the street beside the town walls. How strange — the whole town is still surrounded by these medieval stone walls. Opposite one of the gates, the Porte du Rhône, we find the repair shop. We are lucky — it's open on a Sunday.

"What you really need is a new tube," the mechanic tells me, after he has taken mine out of the tire. "The hole here is getting a bit big for repairing."

"*Eh bien*," I answer, "put a new one in, then. How much is a very good one, please?"

"Seven *francs*," he tells me.

When I reach into my back pocket, my wallet isn't there.

"Oh, I left my wallet in my other pants! Jacques, please lend me seven *francs* till tonight."

"Lend you seven *francs*! All I still have on me is five *francs* and a few *centimes*." And he gives me a *very* dirty look.

"What now, boys?" The man starts to get impatient.

"Just patch it up, please," I say. "Do you think I can make it to Aix and back?"

"Miracles always happen, my friend, but I wouldn't count on one with a tube like that one. Aix is about sixty kilometers from here — no, I wouldn't advise you to count on a miracle. Have you been here in Avignon before?"

"No. But my friend knows it."

"Then why doesn't he show it to you? The Palace of the Popes, the Pont d'Avignon, the Tower of Philippe the Fair — there's a lot to see here!"

"A lot I care if there's a lot to see here," Jacques rails, when we are on the street again. "Have you really never been here?"

"*Non*, really not. But why don't *you* go on to Aix-en-Provence?"

"Oh, don't talk nonsense. We started out together, we stick together, *c'est ça*. Come on, *monsieur*, we now enter the beau-ti-ful ancient city of Avignon, situated so beau-ti-fully on the beau-ti-ful banks of the beau-ti-ful river Rhône . . ." and he mimics a silly tourist guide he has seen in a movie.

We ride through the Porte du Rhône, and turn right. They seem to have only one-way traffic here. Slowly we ride through the town. One of the street signs reads RUE LOUIS PASTEUR, but most of the other street names don't mean anything to me.

The streets are full of people and cars. Along the main boulevard there are open-air restaurants and sidewalk cafés. It is cool and shady here. The tall plane trees on both sides of the street have grown in a strange way. Their crowns meet above the middle of the street — it looks like a tremendous vaulted tent.

A few more turns, and a wide square opens before us. *Mon Dieu*, but this is magnificent! One whole side of the square is taken up by the front of a giant castle.

"This is the Palace of the Popes, *n'est-ce pas*, Jacques? But it doesn't look like a palace at all. It looks like a fortress."

"I think it was built as a fortress. Look up — the old parapets and

watchtowers are still there. But I don't know enough about it. Let's go ask the gatekeeper over there."

We park our motorcycles among the hundreds of cars in the square, and walk up the ramp. First, Jacques buys a picture postcard for each of us at the ticket booth. They show the Palace and the seven popes who once resided here.

"That leaves me with three *francs*," Jacques laughs, "and you owe me two *francs* and seventy *centimes*."

"*Monsieur*," he asks the gatekeeper who stands at the ticket booth, "could you please tell us a bit about the Palace? My friend here wants to know why the popes built a fortress in the middle of the town."

"I'll explain it with pleasure," the gatekeeper answers. "This is not the middle of the town. Here we are on a rock plateau at the edge of the town and about sixty meters above it, high above the Rhône River.

"What made Avignon so famous were of course the seven popes who lived here. In those days, palaces for all the cardinals and bishops and the papal courtiers were built here and across the river."

"Why did the popes leave Rome at all?" I want to know.

"There was much strife going on in Rome at the time. The King of France — his name was Philippe the Fair — had taken the Pope prisoner and had helped a Frenchman to become the new Pope — Clement V, that was. '*Bon!*' the King must have thought, 'as we have a French pope at last, I'd rather have him close to me, where I can make him do as I like, more or less. Why not make Avignon the new papal residence?'

"The King, by the way, was not only handsome. He was also cruel, greedy, and a tyrant. The new Pope didn't dare say '*Non.*' He moved to Provence in the year 1309, and his successors built this palace. In those times, the finest palace wasn't worth much if it wasn't also a fortress, with thick walls and watchtowers. Seven popes resided here, all of them Frenchmen. During this time, the Palace was besieged twice by furious bands of plundering soldiers. So it was good that the popes built a fortress, *n'est-ce pas?*"

"Was it the popes who built the Pont d'Avignon too?" I ask.

"Oh, *non,* that was earlier, in the twelfth century. You know of course that legend about Saint Bénezet, who started it?"

"*Oui! Mille mercis, monsieur!*" we say. "A thousand thanks!" and we walk down the ramp. We ride out from the walled town again and

cross the new bridge over the Rhône River. A road leads down from it, and we follow it.

We park our motorcycles at an ice-cream stand, lock them, and walk along the river bank. From here, I can clearly see that the Palace of the Popes and the cathedral to its left are really built on much higher ground than the rest of the town.

"Do you know why they didn't rebuild the old bridge, Jacques?"

"*Non.* I think they gave up when the spring waters came rushing down and destroyed it again and again. It must have been boring to start all over again every few years. It had seventeen arches, if I remember right, and only three are left. By the way, I said I remember the legend about the bridge, but I really don't. Do you?"

"Bénezet was a shepherd, that's how my mother told us the legend. An angel stopped him once and gave him the order to build a bridge over the Rhône. The Bishop of Avignon and the governor of the town sneered at him and called him a fool. 'You can build a bridge over the river the way you can rip out a rock from the ground,' they said to him. *Bon,* Bénezet ripped out the next rock he saw and threw it down to the bank of the Rhône — and that was the foundation stone of the first arch. The people believed in him and gave him contributions,

and the building began. In the end, the bridge had seventeen arches, and I think it was about nine hundred meters long. It took them ten or twelve years to build it, but they succeeded."

"And why are you grinning while you tell me this?" Jacques asks.

"Ah, *bon,* it is funny, really. I remembered what I said only yesterday to the children at school, when they teased me. 'I am going to the Bridge of Avignon to play *boule,*' I said. *Bon,* I am not playing *boule,* but at least I have gone to the bridge. I am really very glad we came here."

We walk back to our motorcycles, whistling the tune of *"Sur le pont d'Avignon."*

"Do we still have time to go over to the Tower of Philippe the Fair?" I ask Jacques.

"Certainement. It is only a detour of one kilometer or so on our way home."

We ride back to the new bridge and cross to the other side. There we turn right and are soon at a field where gypsies have their camp. Behind it rises the Tower.

"It looks like a chimney up there," I say.

"There is a spiral staircase inside," Jacques explains. "This tower guarded the approach to the bridge. Anybody in possession of the Tower had power over the bridge — and over Avignon, of course."

I dismount and check my back tire. The gypsies seem to be away, but a famished dog barks at me like mad.

"Take it easy, Philippe," I call to him. "I won't attack your tower. I'm busy enough with my back tire."

We ride another few hundred meters, and stop again. Above the houses, a powerful fortress with twin towers looks down on us.

"That's the fortress the kings built at the time of the Popes of Avignon — the fourteenth century, wasn't that what the gatekeeper said? The Tower was sort of an outpost of the fortress here, as far as I know. But I've had enough history for a single day. Let's head for home," Jacques says.

As soon as we are in the open country, a strong mistral comes up.

71

I have to take a hard grip on my handlebars. Even so, the wind pushes me to the left side of the road.

"I don't mind the mistral today!" I shout over to Jacques. "There was so much rain last week, it made the ground in the vineyards too wet. I felt it when I was plowing yesterday. The mistral will dry the ground now."

"Like the Flood do I need the mistral!" he shouts back through the roaring wind. "Look over there at the reeds — that's almost a storm. It will rip off a lot of telephone wires. You won't have to climb up the poles like a monkey and repair the torn telephone wires, but I will!"

"*Chacun à son goût!*" I shout back. I don't know whether that expression fits just now, but I really like it.

The road turns south and now the wind blows ferociously from the back.

The crowns of the cypress trees are swaying back and forth, the reeds in the fields are bending over, and twigs and branches keep sailing down on the road.

At last we arrive at our tall cypress tree below the rocket-firing station. Here we part.

"*A bientôt*, Jacques!" I shout through the wind.

"*A bientôt*, Denis! And don't you turn up next time without a new tube in your tire!"

"I won't!" I call back, and we wave to each other, while we speed on our different ways at the crossroads.

When I pass the *mairie* in our village, I see Yves sitting on the steps with his friends. These steps are a sort of meeting place for the men of the village; a few people are always there to sit around and talk about things.

"*Bonjour*, Denis!" Yves calls over. "Did you do the whole trip like that?"

"Like what?"

"With not enough air in your back tire. I bet you didn't even notice it." And the others make jokes about my back tire too.

"Are you sure your eyes are all right?" I call back. "I didn't notice anything!" And I ride on.

On the way to our house, I see Jean-Pierre sitting on some logs, painting.

"You look like a vagabond," he greets me, "with your hair all tousled."

"If you were riding a Mobylette in this mistral, you would look even worse," I answer, while I take out my comb.

"Mistral? Where is the mistral?" he asks, playing innocent. Of course he sees the mistral in the trees in front of him, but he is protected from it by a north wall at his back. But then he admits it.

"I know there's a mistral on, Denis — that's why I came here. It

cannot catch me in this place, but I try to catch it . . . how do you like my painting?"

"Not bad," I say. "Your cypress trees really *do* sway in the wind. Very good, Jean-Pierre. You know, I am sure you will do it one day, be a painter in Paris. I really think so. *Alors*, I have to go. I don't want to miss the *boule* match."

"Oh, Denis," Maman greets me, "I am glad you are back. Roland is up on the roof. The mistral has torn loose a few roof tiles. Go up and help him make them fast again."

I climb through the attic window, and together with my brother I fasten down the roof tiles.

"Five o'clock!" Roland says. "Let's go. Papa will be waiting for us. We want to win today."

Jean-Pierre has come back too, meanwhile, and together we walk off to the *boule* match.

Glossary

A bientôt   See you soon

Alors   Now, now then, then

Aubergines   Eggplants

Au revoir   Goodbye, I'll be seeing you

Bien; eh bien   Well; well then

Bon; c'est bon   Good, well; that's good

Bon appétit!   Good appetite!

Bonjour   Good day

Bonne nuit   Good night

Boucherie   Butcher's shop

Boulangerie   Bakery, bakery shop

Boule   Ball, a game played with metal balls

Centime   One hundred *centimes* equal a *franc*

Certainement   Certainly

C'est bon   That's good

C'est ça   That's it

C'est comme ça   That's how it is

C'est drôle   That's funny

C'est tout   That's all

C'est vrai   That's true

Chacun à son goût   Everybody to his own taste

Comment ça va? — Ça va.   How goes it? How are you? — All right.

Confiture   Preserves

Curé   Priest

D'accord   Agreed

Déjeuner   Lunch

Dîner   Dinner

Écoute!   Listen!

Entendu   Agreed

Entrez!   Come in!

Fête   Festival, holiday

Flûte   Long thin loaf of bread

Formidable   Excellent, phenomenal

Franc   French currency. Five *francs* equal about one dollar

Garde champêtre   Country policeman

Grand-père   Grandfather

Halte!   Stop!

Kilometer   0.62137 miles. Unit of distance measurement used in France.

Ma chérie   My dear, my darling

Madame   Mrs., madam

Mademoiselle   Miss

Maire   A mayor

Mairie   Mayor's office

Mais   But

Merci, merci beaucoup   Thank you, thank you very much

Merveilleux   Marvelous

Meter   39.37 inches. Basic unit of measuring system used in France.

Mille mercis!   A thousand thanks!

Mobylette   Small motorcycle (brand name)

Monsieur le maire, Monsieur le curé, etc. Polite way of addressing a mayor, a priest, etc.

Mon Dieu!   My God!

Monsieur   Mr., sir

N'est-ce pas?   Isn't that so?

Non   No

Oh là là!   Exclamation of surprise

Oui   Yes

Parfait!   Perfect!

Pas mal   Not bad

Pique-nique   Picnic

Pot-au-feu   Stew

Professeur   Professor

République Française   French Republic

Salle   The living-dining-kitchen room

Tonnerre de Dieu!   God's thunder!

Tricot   Sweater

Un, deux, trois!   One, two, three!

Voilà!   There! There you are!

Postscript

FRANCE has an area of about 213,000 square miles, approximately one-eighteenth the size of the United States. It has eighty-nine counties, or governmental departments, as they are called; the ninetieth is the Mediterranean island of Corsica, where the Emperor Napoleon I was born and grew up. France is the largest country in Europe — almost eighteen times larger than Switzerland — and has, in addition, overseas territories and affiliated countries in many parts of the world. The country's geographical, political, economical, and cultural center is Paris.

France has a great variety of landscapes, from wide flatlands to rugged hill country to the snow-covered Alps that include Mont Blanc (18,782 feet), Europe's highest peak. The Mediterranean Sea gives southern France its warm sunny climate, while the Atlantic Ocean on the western seaboard brings cooler winds and rain to the fertile plains in the north.

A rich country, France exports iron and steel, machinery and cars, textiles, women's fashions, silk, perfume, wheat, vegetables, fruit, and the world's best wine. French taste and French manners, French cookery and French furniture have for centuries set standards, and so has French art. After Greek and Roman art and architecture had dominated Europe for more than fifteen hundred years, it was the artists of medieval France who created a new vision: Gothic art. In the late nineteenth and early twentieth centuries, the painters Daumier, Corot, Manet, Gauguin, Cézanne, Renoir, and Van Gogh won international respect and admiration for French painting. The sculptures of Auguste Rodin have been compared to those of Michelangelo. Georges Bracque, Pablo Picasso, Marc Chagall, and André Derain are amongst the greatest painters of our own time.

The French have been creative in other fields as well. The great philosopher Pascal invented an adding machine in 1642; the phosphorus match, the sewing machine, and the thermometer are French inventions; so are the bicycle, the electric motor, the passenger balloon, black-and-white and color photography, and the movie camera, to name only a few. The scientist Louis Pasteur experimented with bacteria and led the way to controlling diseases such as tuberculosis, diphtheria, typhoid, and yellow fever. In 1896 Henri Becquerel discovered radioactivity in uranium, which marked the beginning of the atomic era.

The First Republic of France, modeled after the newborn United States of America, was founded in 1793, four years after the French Revolution had overthrown the monarchy. The Fifth Republic of France was established in 1958 under the leadership of General Charles André Joseph Marie de Gaulle. In between, perhaps the most memorable period in French history was the First Empire of Napoleon I, whose reign lasted from 1804 to 1814.